LAB MANUAL

Science Inquiry

science.glencoe.com

Glencoe

New York, New York   Columbus, Ohio   Chicago, Illinois   Peoria, Illinois   Woodland Hills, California

Glencoe

The **McGraw·Hill** Companies

Send all inquiries to:
Glencoe/McGraw-Hill
8787 Orion Place
Columbus, OH 43240-4027

ISBN 0-07-830853-4

Printed in the United States of America.

3 4 5 6 7 8 9 10   009   08 07 06 05

Contents

To The Teacher

What is inquiry?

The process of inquiry models actual science practice, encourages problem-solving strategies, and develops critical thinking skills. Inquiry gets students actively involved in the learning process by allowing them to determine materials, procedures, and/or the topics and questions they want to investigate.

Inquiry can range from a very structured activity for those students who need more guidance, to a more open-ended approach in which students design the investigations. The inquiry activities suggested in this manual will not look the same in every classroom. We encourage you to modify the suggested activities in a manner that best supports your students.

Why is inquiry important?

Inquiry activities, such as those in *Glencoe's Science Inquiry Lab Manual*, will help students develop educational, career, and life skills. Students learn how to think for themselves, how to solve problems, and how to apply prior knowledge to new situations.

How can this book help?

Glencoe's Science Inquiry Lab Manual is structured to give support to both teachers and students. Important biological concepts are the core of each inquiry activity. Students gain practice in developing and testing their own hypotheses, designing experiments, gathering and analyzing data, and communicating their conclusions to their peers. Teachers are given strategies to guide students who need additional structure and to encourage students who are ready for more open-ended exploration.

Suggestions for Incorporating Inquiry in the Biology Classroom

Inquiry in biology does take extra time, just as it would in a research lab. Here are some ways you might be able to efficiently incorporate inquiry into your classroom.

- At the beginning of the year, plan with students the systems they would like to study and observe over the course of the year (plants, animals, etc.). Have students identify time constraints such as the length of the organism's life cycle and the availability of the organisms throughout the year. Set up long-term experiments and projects with your students to take advantage of the life cycle and availability of the chosen organisms.

- Supply various materials that are related to the concept you are trying to convey and allow students to explore them in groups for about 15 minutes. Have groups brainstorm ideas and list questions they have about those concepts. Have them list materials they will need. As a class or on your own, eliminate those questions that cannot be answered in the classroom. Gather any additional materials that are needed and allow students to begin their explorations the next day or the next week.

- Have students brainstorm questions they would like to explore. As a class, choose 1 or 2 reasonable questions that each group will explore in its own way. (This is very helpful if you are trying to cover a specific topic.)

- Give your students a more guided activity that relates hard-to-understand concepts and skills. Then, allow them to explore on their own with a wider variety of materials. Make sure you allow time for debriefing so the students (and you) will understand what they learned from the experience.

- Students will need practice doing inquiry before they should be allowed to explore completely on their own. Be sure to give them lots of practice in using the tools of science so that their explorations are more successful.

- Encourage students to rely on their data and not on what they think the answer should be. If their data are unexpected, help them to problem-solve what might have happened.

Correlation to Glencoe Biology Programs

The activities in *Glencoe's Science Inquiry Labs* coordinate with the following chapters/units in these Glencoe biology programs. Use this chart to help plan the best way to use these activities with your class.

	Biology: The Dynamics of Life	Biology: An Everyday Experience	BSCS Biology: A Molecular Approach	Biology: Living Systems	Biology: A Community Context
Activity 1: What is inquiry?	Chapters 1, 2, 18	Chapters 1, 4	Chapter 2	Chapters 2, 27	Unit 1
Activity 2: Monitoring a Plankton Bloom	Chapters 2, 3, 4, 19	Chapter 30	Chapter 25	Chapters 28, 29	Unit 3
Activity 3: Plasma Membranes	Chapters 6, 35	Chapter 9	Chapters 1, 2	Chapters 3, 20	Unit 4
Activity 4: Predicting the Traits of Offspring	Chapters 10, 12	Chapter 26	Chapter 13	Chapter 8	Unit 5
Activity 5: Discovering Your Learning Style	Chapter 36	Chapter 15	Chapter 21	Chapter 25	Unit 6
Activity 6: Plant Adaptations	Chapters 3, 21	Chapters 6, 21, 29	Chapter 11	Chapters 13, 16	Unit 1
Activity 7: Effects of Ozone Depletion	Chapters 2, 21, 23	Chapters 21, 32	Chapter 25	Chapter 30	Unit 2 Unit 8
Activity 8: Measuring Biodiversity	Chapter 5	Chapters 30, 31	Chapter 25	Chapter 12	Unit 7
Activity 9: Effects of Water Quality Changes on Protists	Chapters 2, 5, 19	Chapters 5, 32	Chapters 18, 25	Chapters 15, 30	Unit 2
Activity 10: Environmental Effects on Tadpole Upbringing	Chapters 2, 30	Chapters 8, 30	Chapter 24	Chapters 19, 28	Unit 3

Safety and Disposal of Lab Materials

Teaching science requires the use of certain supplies and safety equipment to maintain a safe classroom. The activities in *Glencoe's Science Inquiry Lab Manual* minimize dangers in the laboratory. Even so, there are no guarantees against accidents. For additional help, refer to the booklet *Glencoe Laboratory Management and Safety in the Science Classroom,* which contains safety guidelines and masters to test students' lab and safety skills.

General Guidelines

- Post safety guidelines, fire escape routes, and a list of emergency procedures in the classroom. Make sure students understand these procedures. Remind them at the beginning of *every* lab session.
- Understand and make note of the safety symbols used in the activities.
- Have students fill out a safety contract. Students should pledge to follow the rules, to wear safety attire, and to conduct themselves in a responsible manner.
- Know where emergency equipment is stored and how to use it.
- Perform all activities before you allow students to do so.
- Supervise students at all times. Check assembly of all setups.
- Instruct students to follow directions carefully and to not take shortcuts or switch steps.
- Make sure that all students are wearing proper safety attire. Do not permit wearing contact lenses, even with safety glasses; splashing chemicals could infuse under a lens and cause eye damage.

Handling Electronic Equipment

- Instruct students on the safety guidelines provided by the manufacturer of your calculator(s) and probe(s).
- Check wiring for damage before each use. Do not use if frayed.
- Do not use the equipment where it could get wet.
- Do not allow students to eat or drink while using the equipment.
- Unplug the calculator when not in use.

- Caution students to use care when handling the equipment. Calculators and probes should not be shaken or dropped.
- Store the equipment properly when not in use.

Handling Chemicals

- Always wear safety goggles, gloves, and an apron when handling chemicals. Treat all chemicals as potentially dangerous.
- Never ingest chemicals. Use proper techniques to smell solutions.
- Use a fume hood when handling chemicals that are poisonous or corrosive or that give off a vapor.
- Know the location of an eyewash station. Flush the eyewash for five minutes once a week to remove harmful contaminants that may grow in the eyewash. Do not use a squeeze bottle as a substitute for an eyewash.
- Always add acids to water, never the reverse.
- Prepare solutions by adding the solid to a small amount of distilled water and then diluting with water to the volume listed. If you use a hydrate that is different from the one specified in a particular preparation, you will need to adjust the amount of hydrate to obtain the correct concentration.
- Consider purchasing premixed solutions from a scientific supply house to reduce the amount of chemicals on hand.
- Maintain appropriate MSDS (Materials Safety Data Sheets) in the laboratory.

Chemical Storage

- Use wood shelving, rather than metal, that is firmly attached to the wall.
- Equip shelves with a lip to prevent chemicals from being jarred off the shelf.

Copyright © by Glencoe/McGraw-Hill, a division of the McGraw-Hill Companies, Inc.

- Store only those chemicals you intend to use.
- Store chemicals in upright positions no more than three containers deep.
- Store chemicals at or below eye level but not on the floor.
- Make sure all containers are labeled to identify the contents, concentration, date purchased or prepared, safety precautions for handling, expiration date, and manufacturer's name and address.
- Separate chemicals by reaction type. For example, store acids in one place and bases in another. Store oxidants away from easily oxidized materials.
- Store flammables in an approved flammable cabinet.

Chemical Disposal

- Maintain an ongoing chemical inventory. Remove chemicals that are out-of-date, contaminated, or lacking legible labels.
- Consult local and state authorities for disposal methods. Use a reference such as *Prudent Practices in the Laboratory: Handling and Disposal of Chemicals* (National Academy Press, 1995) for general guidelines on handling and disposing of chemicals. Current laws in your area supersede the information in this book.
- Neutralize any substance that has a pH less than 3 or greater than 8 before disposal.

- For substances that can be flushed down a drain, flush with at least 100 times its volume of tap water.
- Consider utilizing a commercial chemical disposal company.

Chemical Spills

- Maintain a clearly identified spill kit in the science lab that contains commercial materials for that purpose. You also can keep a container of dry sand or dry clay available; remember that these will not neutralize an acid or base.
- Contain the spill and neutralize the chemical if necessary.
- Remove the material with equipment made of plastic or polypropylene to prevent reaction with any chemical that remains.
- Place the material in plastic bags or containers and label appropriately.
- Inform the custodial staff of proper disposal of the material.
- For a major spill, such as breaking a liter bottle of hydrochloric acid, take the following actions:
  ➤ Evacuate all students through the exits farthest from the spill.
  ➤ Assist any person splashed with the chemical to the safety shower.
  ➤ Contain the spill wearing proper protective clothing. Do not allow the spill to trap you.
  ➤ Call for help.

DISCLAIMER

Glencoe/McGraw-Hill makes no claims to the completeness of this discussion of laboratory safety and chemical storage. The information presented is not all-inclusive, nor does it address all of the hazards associated with the handling, storage, and disposal of chemicals, or with laboratory practices and management.

Science Inquiry Materials Supply List

Activities	Everyday Materials	Lab Materials
Activity 1 **What is inquiry?**	dry soil rubber bands plastic wrap various leaves newspaper small slices of apple, banana, and potato peel	large beakers (2) goggles wax pencil plastic gloves small jar mask moisture meter thermometer distilled water pH meter or pH paper
Activity 2 **Monitoring a** **Plankton Bloom**	nylon stocking scissors plastic tie wire/wire hanger wire cutter pliers needle and thread stapler watch rubber band tap water small plastic container with lid medium-size container with lid heavy-duty tape (duct or mailing tape)	thermometer pH test strips nitrate test kit phosphate test kit 1-mL pipette coverslip rubbing alcohol compound microscope microscope slide/depression slide references for phytoplankton and zooplankton identification
Activity 3 **Plasma Membranes**	beet roots dry yeast salt liquid detergent plastic knife	24-well microplate timer balance hot plate stirring rods pipettes 150-mL beaker methanol distilled water pH paper Congo red biological stain
Activity 4 **Predicting the Traits** **of Offspring**	individuals to observe (people or pets)	fast-growing plants successive generations of plants soil fertilizer
Activity 5 **Discovering Your** **Learning Style**	white index cards tray colored index cards dictionary colored pens or pencils highlighters table of random numbers tape player or CD player with headphones stopwatch/watch or clock with a secondhand two CDs or tapes of different types of music common household or classroom items	
Activity 6 **Plant Adaptations**	soil sand small pots or polystyrene cups	aquatic plants desert plants houseplants 200-watt lamp microscope microscope slides aquarium or large clear container
Activity 7 **Effects of Ozone** **Depletion**	soil scissors water plastic planters heavy-duty string wooden stakes clock/timer ruler	balance drying oven thermometer UVB light source UVB screen fertilizer 500-mL beaker seeds for several species of plants, or partially grown plants

Activities	Everyday Materials	Lab Materials	
Activity 8 **Measuring** **Biodiversity**	heavy-duty string meterstick scissors small garden shovel or trowel	70% isopropyl alcohol collection jars microscope slides 60-watt lightbulb ring stand compound light microscope or dissecting microscope small weights or stakes	dropper magnifying glass sieve paper funnel 500-mL beaker
Activity 9 **Effects of Water** **Quality Changes on** **Protists**	glass jars silt or sand hot water bath vinegar	thermometer microscope slides protist-slowing agent houseplant pesticide culture media for protists cultures of a variety of freshwater protists, such as *Euglena gracilis* compound light microscope	droppers motor oil pH test strips liquid fertilizer

Activity 10
Environmental
Effects on Tadpole
Upbringing
	dried leaves
	lettuce, spinach, and other food for the
	  tadpoles
		water thermometer
		small fish net
		200-watt lamp
		aquariums or short, wide plastic
		  containers with snap-on lids
			magnifier
			tadpoles

Suppliers

American Science & Surplus
P.O. Box 1030
Skokie, IL 60076
1-847-647-0011
www.sciplus.com

Bio-Rad Laboratories
2000 Alfred Nobel Dr.
Life Science Group
Hercules, CA 94547
(800) 876-3425
www.biorad.com

Carolina Biological Supply Co.
2700 York Road
Burlington, NC 27215
(800) 334-5551
carolina.com

Edmund Scientifics
60 Pearce Ave.
Tonawanda, NY 14150-6711
(800) 728-6999
www.scientificsonline.com

Fisher Science Education
4500 Turnberry
Hanover Park, IL 60133
(800) 955-1177
fisheredu.com

Nasco Science
901 Janesville Avenue
P.O. Box 901
Fort Atkinson, WI 53538-0901
(800) 558-9595
www.nascofa.com

Nebraska Scientific
3823 Leavenworth St.
Omaha, NE 68105-1180
(800) 228-7117
nebraskascientific.com

PASCO Scientific
10101 Foothills Blvd.
Roseville, CA 95747-7100
(800) 772-8700
pasco.com

Sargent-Welch/VWR
Scientific Products
P.O. Box 5229
Buffalo Grove, IL 60089-5229
(800) SAR-GENT
www.sargentwelch.com

Ward's Natural Science Est.
5100 W. Henrietta Road
P.O. Box 92912
Rochester, NY 14692-9012
(800) 962-2660
www.wardsci.com

Contents

To the Student

What is inquiry?

When a scientist plans an experiment to help find a cure for cancer, that is inquiry. When a researcher is interested in the behavior of elephants and decides to spend a year observing and describing their social patterns, that is inquiry.

As a student, you may not always get to choose exactly which topic you want to study, but in practicing science as inquiry, you do have the power to plan materials and procedures. And, if you are really curious about something you have observed, your teacher would probably encourage you to investigate that scientific question.

How to Use This Lab Manual

Glencoe's Science Inquiry Lab Manual provides you with a variety of activities about a range of biology topics. Each lab provides you with background material about a topic, offers suggestions for questions to explore, encourages you to form your own questions and hypotheses, and provides you with suggestions for testing your hypothesis. The questions at the end of the lab give you an opportunity to analyze your data and draw conclusions about what you found.

Suggestions for Successful Inquiry in Biology

Conducting inquiry in biology is challenging but it can also be a lot of fun. Here are some ideas for how you can make each inquiry a success:

- **Explore safely.** Always check your plan with your teacher before you get started.
- **Ask questions.** Think about what the activity is asking you to do and make sure you understand it before you begin.
- **Keep an open mind.** Experiments don't always turn out the way you plan them. Use the data you have to draw conclusions. If the result is completely unexpected, try to figure out what you can change to get the results you expected.
- **Be creative.** Think of new ways to explore the concepts rather than the ones that are suggested. This will keep you more interested in the process and can result in some interesting findings.
- **Ask more questions.** Really interesting things can happen during an experiment. Find out why. Explore on your own or get permission from your teacher to extend your project.

Laboratory and Safety Guidelines

Emergencies

- Inform the teacher immediately of *any* mishap—fire, injury, glassware breakage, chemical spills, and so forth.
- Know the location of the fire extinguisher, safety shower, eyewash, fire blanket, and first-aid kit. Know how to use this equipment.
- If chemicals come into contact with your eyes or skin, flush with large quantities of water and notify your teacher immediately.

Preventing Accidents

- Do NOT wear clothing that is loose enough to catch on anything. Do NOT wear sandals or open-toed shoes. Remove loose jewelry—chains or bracelets—while doing lab work.
- Wear protective safety gloves, goggles, and aprons as instructed.
- Always wear safety goggles (not glasses) in the laboratory.
- Wear goggles throughout the entire activity, cleanup, and handwashing.
- Keep your hands away from your face while working in the laboratory.
- Remove synthetic fingernails before working in the lab (these are highly flammable).
- Do NOT use hair spray, mousse, or other flammable hair products just before or during laboratory work where an open flame is used (they can ignite easily).
- Tie back long hair and loose clothing to keep them away from flames and equipment.
- Eating, drinking, chewing gum, applying makeup, and smoking are prohibited in the laboratory.
- Do NOT inhale vapors or taste, touch, or smell any chemical or substance unless instructed to do so by your teacher.

Working in the Laboratory

- Study all instructions before you begin a laboratory or field activity. Ask questions if you do not understand any part of the activity.
- Work ONLY on activities assigned by your teacher. NEVER work alone in the laboratory.
- Do NOT substitute other chemicals/substances for those listed in your activity.
- Do NOT begin any activity until directed to do so by your teacher.
- Do NOT handle any equipment without specific permission.
- Remain in your own work area unless given permission by your teacher to leave it.
- Do NOT point heated containers—test tubes, flasks, and so forth—at yourself or anyone else.
- Do NOT take any materials or chemicals out of the classroom.
- Stay out of storage areas unless you are instructed to be there and are supervised by your teacher.

Laboratory Cleanup

- Keep work, lab, and balance areas clean, limiting the amount of easily ignitable materials.
- Turn off all burners, water faucets, probeware, and calculators before leaving the lab.
- Carefully dispose of waste materials as instructed by your teacher.
- With your goggles on, wash your hands thoroughly with soap and warm water after each activity.

Safety Symbols

SAFETY SYMBOLS	HAZARD	EXAMPLES	PRECAUTION	REMEDY
DISPOSAL	Special disposal procedures need to be followed.	certain chemicals, living organisms	Do not dispose of these materials in the sink or trash can.	Dispose of wastes as directed by your teacher.
BIOLOGICAL	Organisms or other biological materials that might be harmful to humans	bacteria, fungi, blood, unpreserved tissues, plant materials	Avoid skin contact with these materials. Wear mask or gloves.	Notify your teacher if you suspect contact with material. Wash hands thoroughly.
EXTREME TEMPERATURE	Objects that can burn skin by being too cold or too hot	boiling liquids, hot plates, dry ice, liquid nitrogen	Use proper protection when handling.	Go to your teacher for first aid.
SHARP OBJECT	Use of tools or glassware that can easily puncture or slice skin	razor blades, pins, scalpels, pointed tools, dissecting probes, broken glass	Practice common-sense behavior and follow guidelines for use of the tool.	Go to your teacher for first aid.
FUME	Possible danger to respiratory tract from fumes	ammonia, acetone, nail polish remover, heated sulfur, moth balls	Make sure there is good ventilation. Never smell fumes directly. Wear a mask.	Leave foul area and notify your teacher immediately.
ELECTRICAL	Possible danger from electrical shock or burn	improper grounding, liquid spills, short circuits, exposed wires	Double-check setup with teacher. Check condition of wires and apparatus.	Do not attempt to fix electrical problems. Notify your teacher immediately.
IRRITANT	Substances that can irritate the skin or mucous membranes of the respiratory tract	pollen, moth balls, steel wool, fiberglass, potassium permanganate	Wear dust mask and gloves. Practice extra care when handling these materials.	Go to your teacher for first aid.
CHEMICAL	Chemicals that can react with and destroy tissue and other materials	bleaches such as hydrogen peroxide; acids such as sulfuric acid, hydrochloric acid; bases such as ammonia, sodium hydroxide	Wear goggles, gloves, and an apron.	Immediately flush the affected area with water and notify your teacher.
TOXIC	Substance may be poisonous if touched, inhaled, or swallowed.	mercury, many metal compounds, iodine, poinsettia plant parts	Follow your teacher's instructions.	Always wash hands thoroughly after use. Go to your teacher for first aid.
OPEN FLAME	Open flame may ignite flammable chemicals, loose clothing, or hair.	alcohol, kerosene, potassium permanganate, hair, clothing	Tie back hair. Avoid wearing loose clothing. Avoid open flames when using flammable chemicals. Be aware of locations of fire safety equipment.	Notify your teacher immediately. Use fire safety equipment if applicable.

Eye Safety Proper eye protection should be worn at all times by anyone performing or observing science activities.

Clothing Protection This symbol appears when substances could stain or burn clothing.

Animal Safety This symbol appears when safety of animals and students must be ensured.

Radioactivity This symbol appears when radioactive materials are used.

Copyright © by Glencoe/McGraw-Hill, a division of the McGraw-Hill Companies, Inc.

Activity 1 — What is inquiry?

Inquiry activities may be structured, guided, or exploratory. During a structured activity, you follow instructions and observe the results. In a guided activity, you are given a problem or question. Then, you work with other students to determine a process for solving that problem. Exploratory activities allow you to investigate a topic in any way you choose. You will use each of these methods to explore how food scraps and leaves decompose.

Possible Materials

Everyday Materials
- dry soil
- small slices of banana peel, apple peel, and potato
- plastic wrap
- rubber bands
- newspaper

- variety of leaves

Lab Materials
- large beakers (2)
- graduated cylinder
- wax pencil
- small jars
- moisture meter

- distilled water
- thermometer
- goggles
- protective gloves
- mask
- pH meter or pH paper

Background

Food scraps, grass clippings, leaves, and paper can decompose into useful organic waste. One way to decompose these items is to combine them in a compost pile. Properties of the compost pile, such as moisture, oxygen, and contents, affect the rate of decomposition. Other properties related to decomposition include temperature and acidity.

Question

How do properties of the compost pile affect the rate of decomposition?

Form a Hypothesis

Think about what you already know about decomposition in a compost pile. Now, make a hypothesis to answer the question above. Write your hypothesis in your Science Journal.

Safety

Always wear goggles, gloves, and a mask when handling decomposing material.

Do not use meat or dairy products in any of your experiments.

Test Your Hypothesis

Part 1: Structured Inquiry—Does moisture affect the decomposition of food scraps?

1. Fill two large beakers or jars with dry soil. Use a wax pencil to label one beaker *Moist* and the other *Dry*.

2. Obtain small slices of banana peel, apple peel, and potato from your teacher. You will need two of each type of food scrap. Copy the data table on page 3, and record the initial appearance of the food scraps.

3. Place one of each type of food scrap into each beaker. Be sure the soil covers the food scraps.

4. Slowly pour 100 mL of water into the beaker labeled *Moist*. Cover both beakers with plastic wrap held tight with rubber bands. Place the beakers in a dark, warm location.

5. After one day, remove the plastic wrap. Pour the contents of the beaker onto cardboard and record the appearance of the food scraps in your data table. Be sure to wear protective goggles, gloves, and a mask while handling the food scraps.

6. Place the food scraps and soil back in the beakers. Add 10 mL of water into the beaker labeled *Moist*. Replace the plastic covering on the beakers and put the beakers back in the dark, warm location. Wash hands thoroughly after science activities.

7. Repeat steps 5 and 6 every day for a week. Afterward, dispose of the materials as directed by your teacher.

Part 2: Guided Inquiry—Do all leaves decompose at the same rate?

1. Discuss decomposition of leaves with your lab partner. Recall times when you have seen decomposing leaves. What did the leaves look like? Did some leaves seem to decompose faster than others? Write your hypothesis.

2. Work with your partner to design an experiment to test your hypothesis. Use a variety of leaves in your study, including deciduous leaves and evergreen leaves. Include leaves from the ground as well as

leaves from trees. Make a list of the different materials you will need for your lab. Think about how you will make your observations. Create a data table for recording your observations and measurements. In your plan, be sure to include any necessary safety measures.

3. Have your teacher approve your plan before you begin.

4. Gather the materials you need for your lab.

5. Carry out your investigation according to your plan.

Part 3: Exploratory Inquiry—How does the rate of decomposition in a compost pile depend on its properties?

1. Think about other properties of a compost pile that affect the rate of decomposition. You may wish to consider the acidity, the temperature, the amount of air or light, and the contents of the compost pile. Are there other properties you could investigate for their effect on decomposition? Are there other tests you could perform to explore the effect of moisture?

2. Make a list of possible experiments you could conduct. Think about whether the materials required are easily available. How long would each experiment take to complete?

3. Work with your lab partner to choose an experiment from your list. Write out the steps that you will follow, and include a list of materials and a data table for recording your observations and measurements. In your plan, be sure to include any necessary safety measures.

4. Have your teacher approve the plan for your experiment.

5. Gather the supplies you need for your investigation. Perform the experiment according to your plan.

Activity 1

What is inquiry? *continued*

Observations

Day	Decomposition of Food Scraps	
	Dry	**Moist**
1		
2		
3		
4		
5		
6		
7		

Interpret Your Data

1. Look at the observations that you made for Part 1, the effect of moisture on decomposition of food scraps. Describe how the appearance of the food scraps in dry soil and moist soil changed throughout the week.

   _____

   _____

   _____

   _____

2. What variable did you test in Part 2? How does that variable relate to the rate of decomposition?

   _____

   _____

   _____

   _____

3. Look at the data that you collected for Part 3. If possible, make a graph using your data. Remember that the independent variable (the factors you changed) will be on the x-axis, and the dependent variable (your observations) will be on the y-axis.

Activity
1 **What is inquiry?** *continued*

Conclude and Apply

1. How did moisture affect the rate of decomposition of the food scraps you tested in Part 1?

_____

_____

2. Do you think that making the soil in Part 1 very wet would increase the rate of decomposition? Explain your reasoning.

_____

_____

3. Write a conclusion about how the property of compost piles that you tested in Part 3 affects the rate of decomposition.

_____

_____

_____

4. Discuss the results you obtained in Part 3 with your classmates. Compare the different properties each group in your class tested. Draw conclusions about the best conditions for a compost pile.

_____

_____

_____

5. Explain how an exploratory activity, such as the one you performed in Part 3, allows you to investigate a topic in more depth.

_____

_____

_____

_____

Going Further

Look back at the procedures that you used in Part 3. How could you improve your procedures?

_____

_____

_____

_____

_____

Activity 2

Monitoring a Plankton Bloom

Plankton are organisms that are found in both freshwater and marine ecosystems. The word *plankton* is derived from the Greek word *planktos*, which means "wandering." Plankton do not have the ability to move against water currents. Plankton drift with existing water movements. Phytoplankton, such as diatoms and dinoflagellates, are primary producers that use carbon dioxide, nutrients, and light to make food. Zooplankton, such as the copepod (copepods are small crustaceans that are usually shorter than 1 mm) shown below, are free-floating animals that feed on phytoplankton.

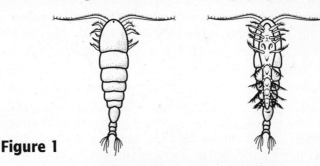

Figure 1

Possible Materials

Everyday Materials
- nylon stocking
- scissors
- small plastic container with lip on the top
- heavy-duty string
- rubber band
- plastic tie
- wire/wire hanger
- wire cutter
- pliers
- thread

- needle
- stapler
- watch
- medium-size plastic container with lid
- tap water
- heavy-duty tape (duct or mailing tape)

Lab Materials
- thermometer
- pH test strips
- nitrate test kit

- phosphate test kit
- rubbing alcohol
- compound microscope
- microscope slide/depression slide
- coverslip
- references for phytoplankton and zooplankton identification
- 1-mL pipette

Background

In temperate regions, seasonal cycles cause changes in the water temperature of lakes and ponds. These changes lead to mixing between surface water and deeper layers of water. This process of mixing, which occurs in both the spring and the fall, is known as turnover. The mixing of water layers results in changes in nutrient concentrations, such as nitrate and phosphate concentrations, as well as oxygen concentrations. These changes have an effect on plankton populations and growth.

Plankton Cycles Plankton exhibit a seasonal cycle that can be monitored using a variety of tools. These tools reveal information about the biological, chemical, and physical characteristics of the water. Plankton cycles are affected by both abiotic and biotic factors, including water temperature, light intensity, nutrient concentrations, and predator-prey relationships. High nutrient concentrations and increasing light intensity in the spring help phytoplankton flourish, resulting in a plankton bloom. Zooplankton populations also will increase after a lag period. To a lesser extent, this process is repeated in the fall, but a fall bloom is usually smaller than a spring bloom because of the decreasing intensity of light.

Collecting Plankton Plankton blooms can be monitored by collecting plankton samples with a plankton net. A plankton net, shown in Figure 2, consists of fine-mesh netting with a collecting cup on one end and a towline on the other end. Acting like a filter, it is pulled through the water. Water passes through the mesh netting, but any organisms larger than the size of the mesh will be collected in the sampling cup. The sample is then analyzed under a microscope and the numbers and types of organisms can be determined. Other measurements, such as water temperature, pH, nitrate and phosphate concentrations, and oxygen concentrations, can be taken as well. In this activity you will construct a plankton net. You will use your net to monitor a fall or spring plankton bloom in a nearby area of water by doing a plankton tow once a week for at least six weeks or longer, if possible.

Question

How do seasonal cycles affect plankton in your area? How can you monitor a plankton bloom?

Form a Hypothesis

Think about what you already know about seasonal cycles and plankton blooms. Now, form a hypothesis to answer one of the questions above. Write your hypothesis in your Science Journal.

Safety ☠ 🚫 ☣ 🧪 🧤 🥽 👔

Wash hands immediately after collecting a sample or working in the laboratory. Do not drink any of the water that you collected. Dress appropriately and wear a personal flotation device if necessary. Use caution while collecting samples. Use all laboratory materials appropriately.

Test Your Hypothesis

1. Think about the materials that have been provided for you. How will you test your hypothesis?

2. Make a list of the steps you will take to monitor a plankton bloom. There are several stages to

consider. First, you will have to construct your own plankton net to use for sampling. Think about how you will use the materials provided to make a plankton net. How will you ensure that it will be structurally strong?

3. Construct your plankton net. Use Figure 2 as a reference.

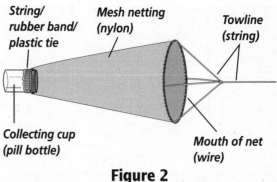

String/
rubber band/
plastic tie

Mesh netting
(nylon)

Towline
(string)

Collecting cup
(pill bottle)

Mouth of net
(wire)

Figure 2

4. Using your knowledge of plankton, make a list of steps you will follow to monitor a plankton bloom.

   • Consider the variables in your experiment.

   • How will you ensure the quality of your data as you make your collections?

- Consider how variations in the following could affect your data:
  - method by which sample is collected (For example: will you have to drag the net through still water, or will the current be strong enough to allow you to hold the net in one place while water passes through it?)
  - length of time of plankton tow
  - time of day sample is collected
  - exact location sample is taken

5. After you collect your data and complete your plankton tow each week, how will you store your sample? Consider the length of time between collection and viewing under the microscope.

Plankton only live for about 24 hours. Store the plankton in the refrigerator or preserve them by adding one part 70% isopropyl alcohol to six parts of water. **CAUTION:** Keep all sources of ignition away from the alcohol.

6. How will you make an accurate count of the organisms in your sample? How will you identify whether an organism is zooplankton or phytoplankton?

7. How will you clean and store your net between uses? Does your net need to be repaired or reconstructed?

8. Read the MSDSs in the test kits and follow the safety guidelines. Review your plan with your teacher before you proceed with each step.

Variable	Week 1	Week 2	Week 3	Week 4	Week 5	Week 6
Surface water temperature (°C)						
pH						
Nitrate (ppm)*						
Phosphate (ppm)*						
Air temperature (°C)						
Weather conditions						
Other observations						
Average number of phytoplankton						
Average number of zooplankton						

* Units may vary depending on test kit.

Interpret Your Data

1. On graph paper, construct graphs that show how the variables of water temperature, pH, nitrate and phosphate concentrations, and the average number of phytoplankton and zooplankton changed over the weeks of sampling. You should also make graphs showing time (week 1, week 2, and so on) on the *x*-axis and the number of phytoplankton and zooplankton on the *y*-axis.

2. Analyze your graphs. How do the seasonal changes correlate to the changes in the number of plankton you collected? Is there a correlation between any other data collected and the number of plankton?

_____

_____

_____

Activity
2 Monitoring a Plankton Bloom, *continued*

Conclude and Apply

1. Do your data support your hypothesis? Explain why or why not.

_____

_____

_____

_____

2. Compare your data to those of your classmates. Are there any differences? What could account for these differences?

_____

_____

_____

_____

3. Explain the relationship between seasonal changes and plankton blooms. How are the concentrations of nitrate and phosphate related to plankton blooms?

_____

_____

_____

_____

4. Predict how nitrates and phosphates from runoff could affect a plankton bloom.

_____

_____

_____

_____

Going Further

If you were to do this project again, how would you improve your methods? What tips would you give to someone who was just beginning the activity?

_____

_____

_____

_____

_____

_____

Activity 3 Plasma Membranes

The plasma membrane of a cell maintains the structure of the cell by enclosing the cell's organelles. They also control which molecules may enter and leave the cells. In this activity, you will investigate how environmental changes may affect plasma membranes.

Possible Materials

Everyday Materials
- beet roots
- dry yeast
- salt
- liquid detergent
- plastic knife

Lab Materials
- methanol
- distilled water
- Congo red biological stain
- pH paper
- 24-well microplate

- 150-mL beaker
- pipettes
- stirring rods
- timer
- balance
- hot plate

Background

Under normal conditions, the plasma membrane protects the cell contents and controls which substances enter and leave the cell. Changes in the environment may alter the structure of the plasma membrane, thereby increasing diffusion of materials into or out of the cell. Environmental changes may also destroy the plasma membrane so that the cytoplasm and organelles inside spill out.

Question

How can environmental changes affect the plasma membranes of a cell?

Form a Hypothesis

Think about what you already know about plasma membranes. Now, make a hypothesis to answer the question above. Write your hypothesis in your Science Journal.

Safety

Wash your hands thoroughly after handling plant material. Be sure not to eat or drink any substances in a lab. Handle glass objects carefully and report any breaks to your teacher immediately.

Test Your Hypothesis

1. Work with your lab partners to make a list of ways that environmental factors can affect plasma membranes. For example, orange crops may be lost when freezing temperatures cause water in the plants to form ice crystals that rupture the plasma membranes.

2. Discuss what effect heating might have on plasma membranes. What would happen if the cells were exposed to salty water, alcohol, or detergents? Are there other chemicals that you could test?

3. One method you might use to study the environmental effects on plasma membranes uses beet roots. Beet cells contain a red chemical. If the plasma membranes are altered or damaged, the red coloring will escape. You can also observe effects on the plasma membranes by looking at yeast cells under a microscope. The chemical stain Congo red normally can't penetrate the membrane of yeast cells. If a solution of yeast cells is stained with Congo red, the cytoplasm will remain clear. However, if the plasma membranes are damaged, the stain will enter the cell and the cytoplasm will appear red.

4. Decide with your lab partner which environmental condition you wish to investigate. Also decide which method you think is best for studying the effect that a change in an environmental condition would have on plasma membranes.

5. Make a list of the steps that you will follow for your investigation. Have your teacher approve your plan.

6. Think about how your environmental change will affect the plasma membranes you test. Record your prediction below.

Prediction: _____

_____

_____

7. Carry out your investigation. You may wish to use a data table similar to the one below. If possible, create a graph of your data.

Data Table

Water Temperature (°C)	Water Appearance

Interpret Your Data

1. Describe the environmental condition that you changed.

_____

_____

_____

_____

Activity 3 **Plasma Membranes,** *continued*

2. Explain the procedure you used to test this environmental change.

_____

_____

_____

_____

3. Using the data table(s) you prepared, describe any changes you observed or measured during your investigation.

_____

_____

_____

_____

_____

4. Describe any problems you may have encountered during your investigation. Did this affect your results? If so, explain how.

_____

_____

_____

_____

Conclude and Apply

1. Review your data table. Write a statement that summarizes your results.

_____

_____

_____

2. Compare your results to those of other groups in your class. Describe other investigations that could be made about environmental effects on plasma membranes.

_____

_____

_____

_____

Activity
3 Plasma Membranes, *continued*

3. The investigations made by you and your class involved only one or a few types of cells. Do you think your results can be extended to other types of plasma membranes as well? Explain why or why not.

_____

_____

_____

_____

Going Further

Describe a way that your investigation or the investigation of another group could be applied to an everyday situation.

_____

_____

_____

_____

Activity 4
Predicting the Traits of Offspring

Children resemble their parents because genes are passed from generation to generation. By examining the traits of a family, you can predict which traits will most likely occur in the offspring. In this activity, you will investigate how traits can be predicted.

Possible Materials

Everyday Materials
- individuals to observe (people or pets)

— or —

Everyday Materials
- soil

Lab Materials
- fast-growing plants
- fertilizer
- successive generations of plants

Background

Traits can be either learned or inherited. Learned traits, such as the ability to read, are acquired throughout our lives. Inherited traits, such as eye color, are determined by genes encoded on DNA in cells. Genes have two or more versions called alleles. One allele might be dominant, and the other might be recessive. A child might show a trait that is not seen in either parent because the child has two recessive alleles for that trait.

Question

How can you predict the traits of offspring?

Form a Hypothesis

Think about your current knowledge of inherited traits. Now, make a hypothesis to answer the question above. Write your hypothesis in your Science Journal.

Figure 1

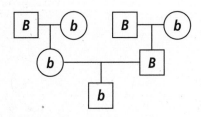

◻ = *Male*   **B** = *Brown eyes*
◯ = *Female*   **b** = *Blue eyes*

Safety

If you are working with plants, be sure to wash your hands thoroughly after handling plants, fertilizer, or other related materials.

Test Your Hypothesis

1. Discuss with your lab partners ways that you could investigate inherited traits. You might want to examine your traits, traits of a family pet, or traits of a plant.

2. After choosing a person, animal, or plant to study, you need to consider from where the traits were inherited. For example, if you choose to examine the traits of a student, you should be able to examine the traits of the student's parents, grandparents, and other family members.

4 Predicting the Traits of Offspring, *continued*

3. Work with your lab partners to write a list of steps that you will follow for your inquiry.

4. Make a list of the traits that you want to study. Remember that some traits are learned and some are inherited. For this inquiry activity, you will consider only inherited traits. Be sure to include any inherited traits, such as blood type and widow's peak, that the people, animals, or plants in your study might have.

5. Have your teacher approve your plan before you begin.

6. Carry out your inquiry according to your plan. When studying the traits of people, plants, or animals, you should complete pedigrees similar to the one in Figure 1. You might also need to prepare a trait survey form similar to the one shown below.

Trait Survey Form

Tongue Rolling	Blood Type	Widow's Peak
__ yes	__ A	__ yes
__ no	__ B	__ no
	__ AB	
	__ O	Earlobe
		__ attached
		__ not attached

Interpret Your Data

1. Look at the trait survey forms that you completed. Note any trends in how the traits are passed on.

_____

_____

_____

_____

_____

2. Draw a pedigree for each trait.

Activity
4 Predicting the Traits of Offspring, *continued*

3. Look at the pedigrees that you drew. Which traits occurred most often? Which traits skipped a generation?

_____

_____

_____

_____

_____

_____

4. What percentage of the people, animals, or plants that you studied had the same form of a specific trait? Calculate the percentage by dividing the number of subjects with the same form of the trait by the total number of subjects.

_____

_____

_____

_____

_____

_____

Conclude and Apply

1. Based on your survey, describe the possible forms that occurred for each trait on your list. What is the probability that each trait will be passed on to the next generation?

_____

_____

_____

_____

_____

2. Compare the results of your inquiry with those of other groups in your class. Based on what you learned, do you feel that it is possible to make a good prediction about the traits a new offspring will have if you know the traits of its recent ancestors? Explain why or why not.

_____

_____

_____

_____

_____

Activity 4 — Predicting the Traits of Offspring, *continued*

Going Further

What do you think was the greatest limitation in your study of inherited traits? What are some ways that you could overcome this limitation in future studies?

_____

_____

_____

_____

_____

_____

_____

_____

_____

Activity 5 Discovering Your Learning Style

Do you often repeat your notes aloud to yourself while studying? You might be an auditory learner. Do you take frequent breaks to get up and move around while studying? You might be a kinesthetic learner. Do you usually form a mental picture of the information that you are trying to remember? You might be a visual learner.

Possible Materials

Everyday Materials
- white index cards
- colored index cards
- highlighters
- colored pens or pencils

- table of random numbers
- common household or classroom objects
- tray
- two CDs or tapes of different music

- tape player or CD player with headphones
- dictionary
- stopwatch/watch or clock with a second hand

Background

How people process and remember incoming information has been a topic of study for many years in the fields of education and psychology. There are several theories or models that exist to help explain how people analyze and catalog new information. One theory of learning style is based on the idea that people interpret and remember information using three modes—auditory or hearing, visual or seeing, and kinesthetic/tactile or moving/touching. Most people use all three modes to process information; however, for many, one mode might be stronger than the other two. For example, some people might find it is easiest to learn new material by hearing it and then repeating it back to themselves. They might find it harder to process new information by just reading the material. People who are strongly kinesthetic might find it is easier to remember if they are moving while they learn. A strongly visual person might prefer to use flash cards or charts and graphs to help him or her learn and remember new information.

Question

What type of learning style(s) do you use?

Form a Hypothesis

Think about how you learn information in the classroom and as you study. Now, make a hypothesis to answer the question above. Write your hypothesis in your Science Journal.

Safety

Use all laboratory materials appropriately.

Test Your Hypothesis

1. Think about the materials that have been provided for you. How will you test your hypothesis?

2. Think about the three types of learning listed in the introduction—visual, auditory, and kinesthetic. Design three separate experiments to test each type of learning. Consider how to set up a control for each experiment. Identify what the independent and dependent variables for each experiment will be. The experiments should be designed in such a way that the data from each should be able to be compared to the other two.

3. Here is some additional information that might help you design your experiments.

   a. Visual learners often need to see the material that they are trying to learn in order to feel as though they understand it. They are encouraged to study using brightly colored flash cards to highlight important points while reading and to rewrite notes in brightly colored ink. Visual learners might learn better if they can create a drawing of a concept. They might be distracted by background movements while trying to concentrate.

   b. Auditory learners often need to repeat aloud information that they are trying to learn. They might put information into a song or rhyme to help them remember it better. They might be distracted by background noise while trying to learn.

   c. Kinesthetic learners may remember best when learning is accompanied by some kind of motion such as pacing, exercising, or even standing. They might also benefit from being able to touch any materials that are involved in learning a concept. They often learn best by physically participating in the activity.

4. Have your teacher approve your plan before you begin.

Possible Procedure

1. To test the auditory mode, create a set of index cards that has 12 random numbers (or a list of letters or words) on each card. Have one partner read the numbers in a neutral tone at one-second intervals. Repeat the reading process two more times. The subject has 30 s to repeat as many numbers as possible in the correct order. Calculate and record the percent value of how many numbers the subject can repeat in the correct order. This can be done under three different experimental conditions: a quiet background, a background of fast paced dance music with words, and a background of relaxation music with no words.

For the second phase of the experiment, allow the subject to read the numbers to himself or herself for 30 s and then try to repeat as many numbers as possible in the correct sequence for the three different backgrounds. New index cards should be used each time a subject is tested.

Auditory Mode

	Quiet Background	Music with Words	Music without Words
Read aloud			
Read to self			

2. To test the visual mode, consider using some combination of the white and colored index cards and the highlighters and/or colored pens and pencils to present the numbers/words/letters.

Visual Mode

	Black & White	Highlighted	Colored
Read aloud			
Read to self			

3. To test the kinesthetic mode, use the same presentation that was used by the auditory mode except, this time, the three experimental conditions will be to have the subject sit still in a chair, then stand, and finally, pace the room.

Kinesthetic Mode

	Sitting Still	Standing	Pacing
Read aloud			
Read to self			

4. Another experiment that can be done to test all three modes involves using a tray or list of at least 12 common objects. The visual mode can be tested by having the subject observe the tray for 30 s then removing the tray from sight and recording how many objects the subject can name correctly.

The auditory mode can be tested by reading a list of similar objects and recording how many the subject can recall. The kinesthetic mode can be tested by allowing the subject to touch the items on the tray, then remove the tray from view, and recording how many the subject can recall. Use a different set of items for each portion of the experiment and calculate the percent of objects that the subject was able to recall correctly.

Object Recall

Experimental Condition	Percent of Objects Recalled Correctly
Looking	
Listening	
Touching	

Interpret Your Data

1. Construct graphs that allow you to compare data collected from each experiment.

2. Is your hypothesis supported by the data? Why or why not?

_____

_____

_____

_____

_____

_____

_____

Activity 5 Discovering Your Learning Style, *continued*

Conclude and Apply

1. What conclusion can you reach about your learning style?

_____

_____

_____

_____

_____

2. What factors other than learning style could affect the outcome of the experiment?

_____

_____

_____

_____

3. How can you use what you discovered about your learning styles to your advantage?

_____

_____

_____

_____

Going Further

Design an experiment that will allow you to further refine your understanding of learning styles.

_____

_____

_____

_____

_____

_____

Activity 6   Plant Adaptations

All living things have traits known as adaptations that enable them to survive in their particular environment. In this activity, you will investigate whether a plant's adaptations will allow it to survive in other environments also.

Possible Materials

Everyday Materials
- houseplants
- soil
- sand

Lab Materials
- aquatic plants
- desert plants
- aquarium or large, clear container

- small pots or polystyrene cups
- 200-watt lamp
- microscope
- microscope slides

Background

Plants have certain adaptations that make them well suited for their environments. The leaves of land plants have small openings called stomata to allow for oxygen and carbon dioxide exchange. Most land plants have tubular cells in their stems to transport water, minerals, and nutrients. Land plants have a waxy coating on their leaves to hinder evaporation of water. This coating is thicker on desert plants, where it also serves to reflect excess light and prevent the plant from overheating. Aquatic plants lack some of the characteristics needed for living on land. They have little strengthening tissue in their stems, and their smaller root systems are for anchorage only.

Question

Will a plant's adaptations allow it to survive in a different environment?

Form a Hypothesis

Think about what you already know about plant adaptations. Now, make a hypothesis to answer the question above. Write your hypothesis in your Science Journal.

Safety

Wash your hands thoroughly after handling plant material. Be careful when handling glass objects.

Test Your Hypothesis

1. Choose a plant from the aquatic plants, desert plants, and houseplants your teacher has provided.

Copyright © by Glencoe/McGraw-Hill, a division of the McGraw-Hill Companies, Inc.

2. Discuss with your lab partners the type of environment for which your plant is best suited. Use reference materials to find information about your plant.

3. Observe the characteristics of your plant that you can see without harming it. Are its leaves large or small? What type of stem does it have? What adaptations can you observe that allow your plant to live in its natural environment? Are there other adaptations that you might be able to see with a microscope?

4. What effect would there be on your plant if you placed it in a different environment? Decide with your lab partners which environment you would like to provide for your plant.

5. Look at the list of materials provided for this activity. How can you use these or other materials to provide the different environment?

Write a plan for your investigation. Remember to include details about how long your investigation will last, how you will care for your plant, and what observations you will make.

6. Have your teacher approve your plan before you begin.

7. Carry out your investigation according to your plan. Record daily observations about your plant. You may wish to use an observation table like the one shown below. Write your prediction for how your plant will react to its new environment in the observation table.

8. At the end of the observation period, use a hand lens to look at the plant's roots. Consider how long they are and their appearance. Next, cut apart the plant's stem and view its cells using a microscope. Make notes on any adaptations visible from these observations.

Data Table

Type of Plant _____

Normal Environment _____

Characteristics _____

_____

New Environment _____

Predict how well your plant will survive in its new environment. _____

_____

_____

Day	Observations
1	
2	
3	

Activity
6 Plant Adaptations, *continued*

Interpret Your Data

1. Which type of plant did you study, and what is its natural environment?

2. Name some characteristics of your plant that you feel are important adaptations enabling it to live in its natural environment.

3. Describe the new environment that you provided for your plant.

4. Explain how you cared for your plant.

5. Review the chart you made for observing your plant in its new environment. Did your plant survive well in this environment? Explain.

6. Did your prediction agree with your results? If not, explain.

Plant Adaptations, *continued*

Conclude and Apply

1. Think about your plant's adaptations and how these adaptations enable the plant to survive in its natural environment. Explain how each of these adaptations either helped or hurt the plant in its new environment.

_____

_____

_____

_____

_____

2. Compare your results with those of your classmates. Write a general statement that describes the class results.

_____

_____

_____

_____

_____

_____

_____

Going Further

Create a computer graphics presentation describing your experiment. If possible, include photographs showing the condition of your plant. Be sure to summarize your results.

Activity 7 Effects of Ozone Depletion

Earth's atmosphere consists of many different gases, one of which is ozone. Ozone gas is formed as ultraviolet light from the sun breaks apart oxygen molecules into single oxygen atoms. These single oxygen atoms combine with molecules of oxygen to form ozone (O_3). Although ozone exists in small quantities high in Earth's atmosphere, it plays a vital role in protecting Earth's surface from harmful ultraviolet (UV) radiation, particularly UVB and UVC radiation.

Possible Materials

Everyday Materials
- soil
- water
- plastic planters
- scissors
- wooden stakes
- heavy-duty string

- clock/timer
- ruler

Lab Materials
- seeds for several species of plants, or partially grown plants

- fertilizer
- 500-mL beaker
- UVB screen
- UVB light source
- thermometer
- drying oven
- balance

Background

When substances such as chlorofluorocarbons (CFCs) and halons reach the stratosphere, they can destroy ozone. These gases were once used in the coolant systems of refrigerators and air conditioners as well as the manufacture of aerosol cans and fire extinguishers. Other, natural processes, such as volcanic eruptions that release aerosols into the atmosphere, can also destroy ozone. Satellite measurements of the total atmospheric ozone during the years 1974 to 1993 show an average global decrease in total ozone of about 2% per decade. The eruption of Mt. Pinatubo in the Phillipines in 1991 also had an effect on atmospheric ozone. The aerosols produced by the eruption caused a short-term decrease in globally averaged ozone by about 6% over the years 1991 to 1994. As a result of this decreased ozone coverage, more UVB radiation is reaching Earth's surface. The Environmental Protection Agency estimates that each percent of ozone reduction results in a 1.5% to 2% increase in the amount of UVB radiation reaching Earth's surface.

The medium-length waves of UVB radiation are known to cause damage to DNA that can result in skin cancer in humans and other animals. Exposure to UVB radiation can also increase the risk of cataract development and aggravate certain skin conditions. Immune system function may decrease. Increased exposure to UVB radiation may also negatively affect plant cell DNA and interfere with photosynthesis. The productivity of phytoplankton in oceans and freshwater and of terrestrial plants can also be affected.

Studies on oceanic phytoplankton have shown that exposure to increased UVB radiation can lead to lowered primary production. A change in the species composition of a given area is also possible. The results of studies on water ecosystems have led to investigations which measure the effects of increased UVB radiation on land plants, including crop plants. Some plants may have a higher natural resistance to the damaging effects of UVB radiation. Studies have shown, however, that exposure to increased UVB radiation results in smaller leaf size and reduced growth in some plants. In this activity you will investigate the possible effects of increased exposure to UVB radiation on at least two species of terrestrial plants.

Activity 7   Effects of Ozone Depletion, *continued*

Question

What effect does UVB radiation have on terrestrial plants?

Form a Hypothesis

Think about what you already know about UVB radiation. Now, form a hypothesis to answer the question above. Write your hypothesis in your Science Journal.

Safety

Always wash your hands immediately after handling plant material.

Test Your Hypothesis

1. Think about the materials that have been provided for you. How will you test your hypothesis?

2. Make a list of steps that you will follow. Consider the following questions as you design your experiment:

   - How will you identify which plants are yours and which treatment they are receiving?

- How will you care for the plants in terms of planting, watering, and fertilizing?

- How will you control variables such as the amount of water or fertilizer given to the plants? Do you want to monitor the temperature in the area of each experimental condition?

- Will you set up your experiment to compare plants grown in regular sunlight to those grown under a UVB shield, or to compare plants grown with no or reduced amounts of UVB to those grown with additional exposure to UVB radiation?

- How will you monitor the effects of UVB radiation on the plants? How will you measure growth rate? Through stem height? Number of leaves? Changes in morphology of plant/leaves? Size/length of leaves?

- Consider measuring the total biomass of each plant at the termination of your experiment. What steps will be involved in measuring plant biomass?

- What other observations such as leaf color, texture, or general appearance of the plant might be important?

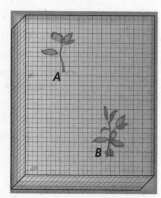

Mesh screen

Sunlight

Sunlight and UVB bulb

- Depending on the number of seeds provided to you, you could extend your experiment to determine at which point in the plant's development the exposure to UVB radiation has the most effect—as a seedling, after germination/sprouting, or after the plant matures.

- You could also consider extending your experiment to see if there is any interaction between increased exposure to UVB radiation and herbivore activity or disease vulnerability in the plants.

3. Review your plan with your teacher. Carry out your investigation. Keep in mind that you must carefully control for other variables in this experiment, such as temperature, moisture, soil type, and nutrients. Slight differences in any of these variables could greatly affect your results. Take careful measurements and notes about the growth and appearance of your plants. You may want to use a table, like the data table below, to help you organize your data.

Data Table

	Week 1	Stem Length (mm)	Number of Leaves	Size of Leaves (mm)	Leaf Morphology	Leaf Color	General Observations
Experimental Condition = Sunlight	Species A						
	Plant 1						
	Species B						
	Plant 1						
Experimental Condition = Sunlight Plus UVB Lamp	Species A						
	Plant 2						
	Species B						
	Plant 2						
Experimental Condition = Mesh Screen	Species A						
	Plant 3						
	Species B						
	Plant 3						

Interpret Your Data

1. Organize your data by making several graphs that show the differences in growth rate, leaf number, leaf size, and biomass of each plant.

2. Analyze your data. Do the results of your experiments support your hypothesis? Explain why or why not.

_____
_____
_____
_____
_____

3. Compare your data from the two species of plants grown. Did one species show more resistance to UVB radiation? What are other explanations for differences in growth between the different species?

_____

_____

_____

_____

Conclude and Apply

1. What effects can UVB light have on terrestrial plants?

_____

_____

_____

_____

2. Studies have shown that increased exposure to UVB radiation leads to decreased primary productivity in phytoplankton. Predict how this could affect all levels of the food chain in an ecosystem.

_____

_____

_____

3. Describe possible solutions that could decrease the impact of increased UVB radiation on crop plants.

_____

_____

_____

_____

4. Design an experiment that would allow you to selectively breed plants that are resistant to the effects of increased exposure to UVB radiation.

_____

_____

_____

_____

Going Further

Prepare your project for presentation to another class. Include information on the current status of the ozone layer and what individuals can do to help further reduce the rate of ozone destruction.

Activity 8 Measuring Biodiversity

Biodiversity is defined as the total variety of life on Earth. The three levels of biodiversity are genetic diversity, species diversity, and ecosystem diversity. Genetic diversity refers to genetic differences both within and between populations. Species diversity, or the variety of species in an ecosystem, is sometimes called species richness. The variety of ecosystems on Earth, ranging from rain forests to deserts to hydrothermal vents, is referred to as ecosystem diversity. In this activity, you will focus on the species diversity of an ecosystem.

Possible Materials

Everyday Materials
- heavy-duty string
- meterstick
- scissors
- small shovel or gardening trowel

Lab Materials
- small weights or stakes

- identification books for plants, fungi, insects and other invertebrates, birds, etc.
- magnifying glass
- collection jars
- ring stand
- paper funnel
- 500-mL beaker

- 70% isopropyl alcohol
- 60-watt lightbulb
- dropper
- microscope slides
- compound light microscope or dissecting microscope
- sieve

Background

Species diversity is the total number of species in an ecosystem, from familiar plants and animals to microscopic bacteria and protists. Some areas of the world, such as tropical rain forests and coral reefs, have higher species diversity than other areas do. For example, a five-square-kilometer area of rain forest in Peru contains over three times as many butterfly species than are found in the entire United States. In this lab, you will compare the species diversity of two different ecosystems in your area. You will survey small areas within each ecosystem using a quadrat similar to the one shown in Figure 1. You may choose to compare any two ecosystems in your area. Examples include a grassy park, a downtown street, a desert, a sandy beach, or a forest. You may also choose to compare any two local aquatic ecosystems, such as a small pond, a tidal pool, a stream, or a large lake.

Question

How does species diversity differ between two ecosystems in your area?

Form a Hypothesis

Think about what you already know about biodiversity and the different ecosystems in your area. Now, make a hypothesis to answer the question above. Write your hypothesis in your Science Journal.

Safety

Always wash your hands immediately after completing field or laboratory work. Wear gloves and appropriate clothing while you conduct your survey. To avoid hazards in conducting field studies, don't reach where you can't see. If the vegetation is higher than one foot, use a stick to check for hidden hazards ahead of you. Avoid wearing perfumed products that will attract insects. Be alert and avoid poisonous plants and animals.

Activity

8 Measuring Biodiversity, *continued*

Test Your Hypothesis

1. Think about the materials that have been provided for you. How will you test your hypothesis?

2. Make a list of steps that you will follow. First, you will have to choose two ecosystems in which to conduct your surveys. Then, you will have to construct your quadrat. Use Figure 1 as a basic guide for quadrat construction. How will you ensure that you are sampling an area within the ecosystem at random?

Figure 1

3. Once you are ready to conduct your survey, consider the following questions:

- Will you sample the soil in each area? See Figure 2 for ideas on how to set up a soil funnel to help you further identify any organisms in the soil sample.

- Will you be sampling any water in each area?

- How will you identify the organisms in your quadrat?

- Will you describe any other details about the area surveyed?

Figure 2

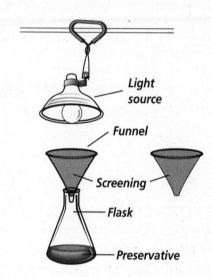

4. Once you have completed your list, ask your teacher to approve your plan.

5. Carry out your investigation. Take careful notes as you conduct your surveys. You might want to use a data table like the one shown below to help you organize your data and calculate species diversity.

Data Table

Organism	Number of Individuals	Proportion of Total Organisms	Square of the Proportion of Total Organisms
Total			

Activity
8 Measuring Biodiversity, *continued*

Interpret Your Data

1. Calculate the biodiversity of each area surveyed using the Simpson Diversity Index.

_____

_____

_____

_____

_____

_____

2. Compare the Simpson Diversity Index values for the two areas that you surveyed. Which area has higher biodiversity? Do your data support your hypothesis? Explain why or why not.

_____

_____

_____

_____

_____

_____

Conclude and Apply

1. Compare and contrast the characteristics of the two ecosystems that you studied. How are the characteristics of each ecosystem related to the species diversity?

_____

_____

_____

_____

_____

_____

2. Compare your data to those of others in the class. What conclusions can be made from the similarities or differences in data?

_____

_____

_____

_____

_____

_____

3. Why is it important to conduct more than one survey within each ecosystem?

_____

_____

_____

_____

4. Explain why monitoring biodiversity is important.

_____

_____

_____

_____

Going Further

Research the influence of human activities on biodiversity. Share the results of your research with your class in the form of a multimedia presentation.

Activity 9 Effects of Water Quality Changes on Protists

Protists (Kingdom Protista) are an extremely diverse group of organisms. They exhibit a number of characteristics that set them apart from bacteria, plants, animals, and fungi. Protists can be one-celled organisms, like bacteria. But unlike bacteria, which are prokaryotes, protists are eukaryotes, and they can be multicellular. Many protists are too small to be seen without a magnifying lens. Others, such as slime molds and the algae that make up kelp forests, can be easily seen and may even be very large. Protists are photosynthetic organisms, and they are heterotrophs that feed on bacteria or other protists. Living in freshwater, salt water, soil rich with decaying matter, and other moist areas, many protists use flagella, cilia, or pseudopodia to move around. Examples of protists you may be familiar with are shown in Figure 1.

Possible Materials

Everyday Materials
- glass jars
- silt/sand
- vinegar
- hot water bath

Lab Materials
- cultures of a variety of freshwater protists including (but not limited to) the following:

  Euglena gracilis

  Amoeba proteus

  Paramecium caudatum

  Synedra

  Volvox globator

  Chilomonas

- culture media for protists
- liquid fertilizer
- pH test strips
- motor oil
- houseplant pesticide
- thermometer
- droppers
- protist-slowing agent
- microscope slides
- compound light microscope

Background

In freshwater ecosystems, protists are important organisms at or near the base of the food chain. Photosynthetic protists contribute to the total amount of primary production. Others provide a link between primary producers and consumers and larger, secondary consumers, such as fish.

Freshwater protists are affected by a number of variables. Runoff, acid precipitation, heavy metals, oil, pesticides, and pollutants can change water quality, which can have an impact on organisms living in the ecosystem. Many times the effects of changes in water quality are noticed in larger organisms because observations, samples, and population counts can be made easily. However, smaller organisms are also affected by the influx of pollutants. In this activity, you will investigate the effects of water quality changes on several species of protists.

Activity 9 Effects of Water Quality Changes on Protists, *continued*

Question
Does a change in water quality affect protists?

Form a Hypothesis
Think about what you already know about protists and how they interact with their environment. Now, form a hypothesis to answer the question above. Write your hypothesis in your Science Journal.

Safety

Always wash your hands immediately after handling chemicals such as pesticides and fertilizers. Wear goggles, gloves, and appropriate clothing while you conduct your experiments using hazardous chemicals. Do not touch your face while conducting science activities.

Test Your Hypothesis
1. Think about the materials that have been provided for you. How will you test your hypothesis?
2. Make a list of steps that you will follow. Consider the following statements and questions as you plan your experiment:
   - Identify the independent and dependent variables of the experiment. How will you maintain a control throughout the

Figure 1

Amoeba   Euglena   Paramecium

experiment? How will you manipulate the independent variable for each experimental condition?
   - How will you monitor the number of organisms in each experimental condition? You will need an initial estimate and frequent estimates throughout the course of the experiment. How often will you determine the number of organisms? Will you return the sampled organisms to the culture after you have examined them?
   - How will you use the materials provided for you to model changes in water quality, such as the addition of nutrients, pesticides, oil, and silt; changes in pH due to acid precipitation; or increased water temperature due to thermal pollution?
3. Once you have completed your list, ask your teacher to approve your plan. Be sure to include any necessary safety measures.
4. Carry out your investigation. Make careful counts of the number of organisms for each experimental condition. You might want to organize your data in a table like the one below. Construct a similar data table for each organism used in the experiment.

Copyright © by Glencoe/McGraw-Hill, a division of the McGraw-Hill Companies, Inc.

Data Table

Estimated Number of Organisms/mL						
Experimental Condition	**Initial**	**Day 1**	**Day 2**	**Day 3**	**Day 4**	**Day 5**
Control						
Vinegar						
Oil						
Silt						
Nutrients						
Pesticide						
Heat						

Effects of Water Quality Changes on Protists, *continued*

Interpret Your Data

1. For each organism tested, use graph paper to make a line graph that shows how the number of organisms changed through time. Label the horizontal axis *Time (days)* and the vertical axis *Estimated Number of Organisms/mL.* Use a different color line to represent the changes through time for each experimental condition. Make a legend to identify which experimental condition each color represents.

2. Analyze your tables and graphs. Were any of the organisms affected by the changes in water quality? Which organisms were most affected? By which experimental condition? Did the results of the experiment support your hypothesis?

_____

_____

_____

_____

_____

_____

_____

Conclude and Apply

1. Compare your data to those of your classmates. How can you explain any differences in data collected by different groups? What can you conclude about the effects of water quality changes on protists?

_____

_____

_____

_____

_____

_____

2. How can you explain differences in results when you compare different species under the same experimental condition?

_____

_____

_____

_____

_____

_____

_____

3. Predict how changes in the protist population of a given body of water could affect other organisms.

_____

_____

_____

_____

_____

4. Can protists be used as bioindicators of changes in water quality? Based on the results of your experiment, which organism would you choose to use as a bioindicator?

_____

_____

_____

_____

_____

Going Further

Design an experiment that will allow you to determine which species of protists are useful as bioindicators.

_____

_____

_____

_____

_____

_____

Activity 10
Environmental Effects on Tadpole Upbringing

As with all organisms, the environment is critical to a tadpole's survival as it matures into a frog. In this activity, you will investigate the best environment for raising tadpoles in captivity.

Possible Materials

Everyday Materials
- dried leaves
- lettuce, spinach, and other food for tadpoles

Lab Materials
- aquariums or short, wide, plastic containers with snap-on lids
- water thermometer

- magnifier
- small fish net
- 200-watt lamp
- tadpoles

Background

The larval stage of a frog's life is a tadpole, also known as a polliwog. Unlike a frog, a tadpole breathes through internal gills. It has no legs, and it propels itself through the water using its tail. Through metamorphosis, a tadpole matures into an adult frog. Its legs develop and, as it grows lungs for breathing out of water, its gills disappear. A tadpole usually eats only plants, but as it transforms into a frog, its digestive system changes, allowing it to eat insects and other small animals.

The successful development of a tadpole depends on its environment. A tadpole needs freshwater, mild temperatures, and the proper amount and type of food. The length of time required for a tadpole to change into a frog varies depending on the species and the tadpole's environment.

Question

What is the best environment for raising tadpoles in captivity?

Form a Hypothesis

Think about what you already know about tadpoles. Now, make a hypothesis to answer the question above. Write your hypothesis in your Science Journal.

Safety

Ask your teacher about proper procedures for handling tadpoles before beginning the activity. Wash your hands thoroughly after handling the plants, water, or tadpoles. Exercise extra caution if your investigation requires the use of a light source near the tadpole habitat. Do not let water splash on hot lightbulbs.

Copyright © by Glencoe/McGraw-Hill, a division of the McGraw-Hill Companies, Inc.

Test Your Hypothesis

1. Before beginning this project, research tadpoles to learn about proper care and feeding. Contact local wildlife experts and ask about regulations regarding obtaining tadpoles and releasing frogs into ponds. Talk with your teacher about where you will obtain the tadpoles and what will happen to the tadpoles or frogs when the project is completed.

2. For this inquiry activity, you will examine the best conditions for raising tadpoles in captivity. Discuss with your lab partners which variable you want to investigate, and which conditions you want to keep constant. You might want to consider the temperature, food, lighting, or number of tadpoles kept in a container.

3. Make a list of the steps you will follow in your investigation. Think about what properties you will observe when determining the tadpoles'

response to various environmental conditions. How long will you observe your tadpoles? Remember that you must use a control group in your investigation. In your plan, be sure to include any necessary safety measures.

4. Have your teacher approve your plan for the activity.

5. Prepare the habitats that you will use for your tadpoles. Be sure to vary only one condition of the environment. When the habitats are ready, obtain the tadpoles according to your teacher's instructions. In your Science Journal, note any differences you find in the tadpoles, for example, species or size. At the end of the experiment, you may want to examine any such differences in relation to your findings.

6. Carry out the investigation of the tadpole's environment. Record your observations carefully. You might want to use a table like the data table below.

Data Table

Tadpole Growth and Well-Being		
Control Group Conditions:		
Experimental Group Conditions:		
Date	**Control Group**	**Experimental Group**

Copyright © by Glencoe/McGraw-Hill, a division of the McGraw-Hill Companies, Inc.

Activity
10 Environmental Effects on Tadpole Upbringing, *continued*

Interpret Your Data

1. How did the condition of the control group of tadpoles change throughout your investigation?

_____

_____

_____

_____

_____

2. How did the condition of your experimental group of tadpoles change throughout your investigation?

_____

_____

_____

_____

_____

3. Did any unplanned events occur during your investigation that might have affected your results? If so, what were they?

_____

_____

_____

_____

_____

4. Make a Venn diagram below comparing changes in the overall conditions of your control group and your experimental group.

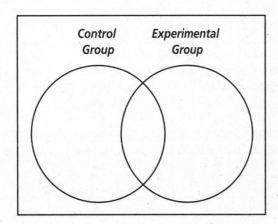

Control Group   Experimental Group

Conclude and Apply

1. Compare and contrast how the conditions of your control group and your experimental group changed.

_____

_____

_____

_____

_____

2. Which group seemed to thrive better? Explain.

_____

_____

_____

_____

_____

3. Summarize the results of your investigation.

_____

_____

_____

_____

_____

4. If you could extend or repeat your investigation, what would you do? Why?

_____

_____

_____

_____

5. Look over the results obtained by other groups in your classroom. Compare your group's results to those of the other groups. Write a summary of what you think are the best environmental conditions for raising tadpoles in captivity.

_____

_____

_____

_____

Going Further

Use computer graphics software to prepare an instructional booklet for raising tadpoles in captivity.

Activity 1

Purpose Students perform activities to explore the effects that different factors have on the rate of decomposition in a compost pile. They learn about the three types of hands-on activities: structured, guided, and exploratory.

Skills Reinforced identifying a question, forming hypotheses, predicting, testing a hypothesis, controlling variables, observing, measuring in SI, making and using tables, recording data, making graphs, recognizing cause and effect, evaluating others' data and conclusions, communicating

Time Required about 20 minutes to set up each of the three activities; five minutes each day for observations (it may take several weeks for students to achieve good results); one period for final measurements and analyzing data

Background A good compost pile should be moist but not dripping wet. Too much water compacts the pile, decreasing the available oxygen, and slowing decomposition. Microbes in the compost need oxygen for the decomposition process. Turning the pile is an easy way to provide this oxygen. A compost pile should contain both nitrogen-rich materials and carbon-rich materials. Nitrogen-rich materials, such as vegetable scraps, coffee grounds, and grass clippings, decompose more quickly than carbon-rich materials, such as brown leaves, twigs, and paper. Temperature and acidity are indicators of the decomposition in a compost pile. The actions of microbes increase the temperature and acidity of compost. As the decomposition process slows, the temperature and acidity decrease.

Possible Procedure Part 1 of the activity guides students in a step-by-step procedure. For Part 2, students will devise an experiment to compare the rates at which different leaves decompose. They probably will place the leaves in different soil-filled containers and monitor the leaf decomposition. Decomposition will probably take longer than for the food scraps in Part 1. In Part 3, the class is presented with a problem to explore: *How does the rate of decomposition in a compost pile depend on its properties?* Students will work in pairs or small groups to decide on a part of the problem to investigate. For example, they might explore how the initial acidity of compost material affects the rate of decomposition. They might also investigate how providing oxygen to a compost pile through turning affects the rate of decomposition.

Preparation Tips

- For Part 1, cut the fruit and vegetable parts ahead of time. Be sure that each group of students has two equal-sized slices of each.
- Obtain a variety of leaves for Part 2. Be sure to include both evergreen and deciduous leaves.
- Use soil that is rich in microorganisms. If possible, obtain soil from a wooded area.
- Small compost piles can be made in jars, beakers, or plastic soda bottles that have been cut in half.

Open It Up Avoid providing students with leading statements about the type of investigations they should choose for Part 3. Instead, encourage students to brainstorm with each other. Have them consider questions that interest them about what they have observed in a compost pile.

Guiding Your Students

- Remind students that the purpose of this activity is to introduce them to inquiry activities. They are given step-by-step instructions in Part 1. In Part 2, they are given a specific problem to investigate, but they must devise their own procedures. In Part 3, each group of students decides which part of a problem to solve. Afterward, they combine their results to draw conclusions about the problem.
- Some students will require additional help in choosing a topic for Part 3. You might wish to have them complete this question: "How does _____ affect the decomposition rate of _____ in compost?"
- Be sure students understand the reasons behind their results. Encourage them to research their topic thoroughly.

Interpret Your Data

1. Students probably will find that food scraps in moist soil decompose faster than those in dry soil. The scraps in the dry soil will maintain more of their original appearance.

2. The variable tested was the type of leaf. In general, deciduous leaves decompose faster than evergreen leaves.

3. Check students' graphs to be sure they transferred information from their data table correctly.

Conclude and Apply

1. It increased the rate of decomposition.

2. No, too much water causes the soil to become deprived of oxygen and slows decomposition.

3. Answers will depend on the property that students test. As an example, students who test for temperature may find that higher temperatures result in faster decomposition.

4. The class might conclude that the best conditions are moist soil, the presence of a variety of materials, and turning the soil to provide adequate oxygen. They might also notice that higher temperature and acidity indicate that decomposition has occurred.

5. An exploratory activity allows students to focus on one aspect of a problem. They learn more about the problem by combining their results with the results of others in the class. A second advantage might be that students could follow up on experimental results by designing another experiment.

Going Further
Remind students that learning from mistakes is an important way scientists increase their knowledge of a subject.

Activity 2

Purpose Students acquire problem-solving experience as they construct their plankton nets and take their samples. Students master important biological concepts as they interpret data and analyze relationships between variables.

Skills Reinforced problem-solving, forming hypotheses, testing hypotheses, controlling variables, measuring, observing, collecting data, developing explanations, communicating

Time Required one period to make plankton net; one period each week to analyze samples; one period to analyze final data; student time outside of class to collect samples

Background The cycles of phytoplankton and zooplankton populations are usually tied together in a classic example of predator-prey interaction. Soon after the number of phytoplankton in an area increases, the number of zooplankton also will increase. As nutrients such as nitrates or phosphates become scarce, the phytoplankton die. As the number of phytoplankton decreases, the number of zooplankton begins to decrease.

Possible Procedure Students cut the toe end of the nylon stocking and attach it to the sampling cup. Bend one piece of wire into a circle by twisting the two ends over each other. The mouth of the net can be made by cutting the nylon stocking at the top of the one leg and

attaching it to the wire. Four pieces of string of equal length are attached equidistant from each other around the mouth. The four loose ends are tied together and one longer piece of string is tied at the knot formed by the other three pieces.

To establish consistency and to be able to make a relative comparison of the number of organisms in each sample, have students remove between 0.1 mL and 0.5 mL of water from each sample to view under the microscope. They then count the number of phytoplankton and zooplankton and attempt to identify some organisms. Students can count the number of phytoplankton and zooplankton for five drops of each sample and take an average for the five drops. After finding the average number of phytoplankton and zooplankton in the portion of the sample examined under the microscope, they can estimate the total number in each milliliter of sample water. Students use these and other data to construct graphs.

Alternate Procedure If your class does not have access to a suitable body of water for this experiment, students can still learn to monitor plankton populations. Kits for culturing plankton in aquariums are available for purchase. These kits can contain both algae and rotifers—organisms that feed on the algae—as well as bottled nutrients that will help the organisms grow. If you decide to culture plankton, encourage students to form a hypothesis about the most favorable growing conditions. The background information still applies—the algae need light and nutrients to flourish. By using two tanks, students can vary one growing condition (for example, the amount of light the tank receives) and compare the results for the tanks. They will need to adapt their plankton nets to the small tank size; otherwise, the procedure for harvesting and counting may be very similar to the one described in the project.

If the kits are too expensive or are not readily available, consider seeding an aquarium with the water from a mature fish tank, which contains many microorganisms. Students can first analyze the water from the mature tank to see which microorganisms it contains. They can then take two fresh tanks, vary one growing condition, and proceed as above.

Preparation Tips
■ Review the concept of turnover and how it affects plankton with students.
■ If applicable, order nitrate, phosphate, and other test kits in advance.

Open It Up Ask students to think of other factors to test. What other questions arise during the project? Allow interested students to pursue these.

Guiding Your Students

■ Encourage students to be creative in attaching the sampling cup. Possible ways it can be attached include wrapping a rubber band, tightening a plastic tie, or tightly tying a piece of string just beneath the lip of the jar.

■ The nylon can be attached to the wire mouth of the net by sewing it or stapling it. Some students may choose to tape the two ends of the wire mouth together after twisting them together.

■ Students could test their completed nets in a basin of water in the lab.

■ Encourage students to learn how to use the net in the water. When a sample is collected, the net should be pulled slowly through water for the designated period of time (approximately 3–5 minutes). If the water has a current, the net can be held in one place for the entire collection time.

Interpret Your Data

1. Check to make sure that students correctly graph the data in their tables.

2. If a fall or spring bloom occurred in the water sampled, graphs should show an increase in the number of phytoplankton and zooplankton, followed by a decrease in the numbers of each over the sampling period. If nitrate and phosphate were tested, the graph should show that as the amount of phytoplankton increased, the concentration of these nutrients decreased. Answers about the correlation of other data and the number of plankton will vary.

Conclude and Apply

1. Hypotheses might include that rising nutrient levels will lead to a phytoplankton bloom. Data showing an increase in nutrient levels followed by increasing phytoplankton counts would support this hypothesis.

2. Differences might result from different water being sampled, human error, random error, or variation in plankton nets, sampling methods, or counting methods.

3. As water temperature begins to rise in the spring, the surface water reaches maximum density and sinks. The deeper water that contains high concentrations of nutrients, such as nitrates and phosphates, rises to the surface. This process is known as spring turnover. The high nutrient concentrations and the increasing intensity of light each day provide conditions that allow phytoplankton to flourish, resulting in a plankton bloom. Zooplankton populations will also increase

after a lag period. When the resources are exhausted, the plankton die. As the surface water cools in the fall, it reaches its highest density, and sinks. Once again, deeper water that contains high amounts of nutrients rises to the surface. A fall bloom is usually smaller than a spring bloom due to the decreasing intensity of daylight.

4. The addition of nutrients from runoff can lead to an increase in the phytoplankton population during the bloom because nutrients are usually the limiting resource in a plankton bloom. The bacterial decomposition of the increased amounts of organic matter from the bloom can cause an unusually high oxygen demand. The resulting hypoxic or anoxic conditions can lead to fish kills.

Going Further

Students might mention using computer applications to graph data as a tip for someone who is beginning the activity. Students might also wonder about how to take exact plankton counts. Have them research gridded slides and counting chambers for plankton.

Activity 3

Purpose Students will learn about how environmental changes can affect plasma membranes.

Skills Reinforced identifying a question, forming hypotheses, testing a hypothesis, observing, measuring in SI, making tables, making graphs

Time Required 45 minutes to plan the activity; 45 minutes to carry out the investigation; 30 minutes to answer conclusion questions

Background A plasma membrane is composed primarily of fats and proteins. High temperatures, detergents, alcohols, salt, and acidity may degrade or destroy the membrane. Under such conditions, substances may be able to pass through the plasma membrane more easily, or the membrane may be destroyed. Freezing may form ice crystals that rupture the plasma membrane.

Possible Procedure Students will choose one method for observing the effects of environmental changes on plasma membranes. They will then choose one or more environmental conditions to apply to the cells. If students use the beet root method of observing effects on plasma membranes, they should cut a small (about 1-cm square) chunk of beet root, rinse it thoroughly, and place it in water (for heating) or the solution to be tested. A color change after a few minutes will indicate if plasma membrane damage has occurred and the cell contents have leaked out. If students use the yeast cell method, they should dissolve a few pinches of dry baker's yeast in water and place a drop of it on a microscope slide. Next, they should add a drop of Congo red stain and observe the cells under a microscope at 400×. Red-colored cytoplasm indicates a structural change in the plasma membrane. Students should use a control for all investigations.

Preparation Tips

■ Prepare yeast stain by adding 0.5 grams of Congo red stain to 100 mL of distilled water.

■ Demonstrate the methods of testing the beet and yeast plasma membranes. You may also need to demonstrate the proper procedure for observing yeast cells under a microscope.

Open It Up Encourage each group to investigate a different environmental condition. During a class discussion, ask questions which will lead them to think of different possibilities. For example, ask, "What effect does acid rain have on a plant?" and "Why do orange growers sometimes lose their entire crops during freezing weather?" Relate these everyday situations to the environmental effects on plasma membranes.

Guiding Your Students

■ You will probably have to work closely with some students if they study the effect on yeast cells. This method of investigation may be better suited to more capable students.

■ If students find that their investigation isn't working well, help them re-evaluate their method. Encourage them to start over if time permits.

Interpret Your Data

1. Students may answer high/low temperatures, detergents, alcohols, salt, or acidity.
2. Answers will vary, but many students will choose to use beet roots and yeast cells.
3. Answers will vary. If studying beet cells, students will mention color changes in the liquid. If studying yeast cells, students will mention color changes in the cytoplasm.
4. Students should be aware of limitations in their investigation.

Conclude and Apply

1. Students will probably find that each of the environmental condition changes affects the plasma membranes to some extent. They should not observe changes in their control cells.
2. Answers will vary, but students may suggest varying temperatures, varying chemicals exposed to the cells, or changing the pH of the cells' environment.

3. Although the results only apply to the cells in this study, most other cells are affected in a similar way. Students should understand that they cannot say conclusively that other cells would react in a similar way without further tests.

Going Further

Have students write their description as a paragraph and present it to the class. If they have trouble thinking of an application, encourage group discussions and further research.

Activity 4

Purpose Students will learn how traits in families can be used to predict the traits of offspring.

Skills Reinforced forming hypotheses, predicting, testing a hypothesis, observing, comparing and contrasting, drawing conclusions, calculating ratios

Time Required 45 minutes to plan the study; time for the inquiry might range from one week for studies of people or pets to 5 months for plant studies; 45 minutes to analyze data and make conclusions

Background An offspring obtains half of its genes from its mother and half from its father. Alleles (different forms of a gene) may be dominant or recessive. The offspring only will have the trait determined by the recessive allele if both of its alleles for that trait are recessive. If the offspring has one dominant allele and one recessive allele for a trait, it is called a carrier. It will have the trait determined by the dominant allele. A carrier can pass either the dominant or the recessive allele to the next generation.

Possible Procedure Each group might choose to investigate traits of members of a family. They will make a list of traits and survey each family member about the traits. Students then will make pedigrees and look for patterns of occurrence for the traits. The class then will compare their results and conclude how easily it is to predict the traits of offspring.

Preparation Tips

■ Discuss a sample pedigree with students to illustrate how traits can be passed from one generation to the next.

■ Some students might choose to study the traits of plants. You can obtain successive generations of plants from nurseries. Alternatively, fast-growing plants are available from biological supply companies. These plants can grow from seeds to mature, seed-bearing plants in about 40 days.

Open It Up Be sure that families, plants, and animals are studied by different groups of the class. As students work through the activity, encourage students to ask "Why?" questions about their inquiry. For example, they might ask, "Why doesn't anyone in the family have black hair?" or "Why do all of the dogs that we studied have long, floppy ears?" Are there other questions about inherited traits that arise? Allow interested students to explore these further.

Guiding Your Students

■ Discourage students from studying too many traits.

■ Remind students that some traits, such as the need for eyeglasses, might be hereditary or might be caused by events in a person's life.

■ Students will not always be able to obtain information by direct observation. For example, they might obtain information about an individual's great-grandparents by asking the individual's parents about the traits.

Interpret Your Data

1. Students probably will notice that some traits have more than one form. Other traits have only one form and may skip generations.

2. Be sure that students' pedigrees are coded to show different versions of traits and the occurrence of traits.

3. Students should consider different versions of individual traits.

4. Answers will depend on the people, animals, or plants that students survey.

Conclude and Apply

1. Students should mention different alleles for traits. They also should mention whether the alleles are dominant or recessive. A probability is the ratio of the number of times a trait occurs divided by the number of individuals in the survey.

2. Students should realize that although traits can be predicted, you can only be certain of an outcome if both parents have the recessive version of a certain trait. They should also realize that some traits may be recessive and will not show up in their survey. Students might also note that, if a pedigree reveals either one or both parents to be homozygous dominant, you can be certain the offspring will express the dominant trait.

Going Further

The major limitation of this study is that students will only survey a few generations of a family. Long-term studies would overcome this difficulty.

Activity 5

Purpose Students will investigate differences in how people perceive incoming information and which senses are used to help process and remember new information.

Skills Reinforced forming hypotheses, controlling variables, testing hypotheses, collecting data, developing explanations, making graphs, communicating

Time Required one period to set up experiments, one period each to conduct experiments for each of the three categories, one period to analyze data

Background Walter Barbe and Raymond Swassing present a theory of learning style and memory based on the idea that there are three fundamental modes used when perceiving, processing, and remembering information. Being aware of strength in a particular mode and incorporating it into his or her learning experience can be useful to an individual.

Possible Procedure Students can work in groups of two, with each partner acting as both the tester and the subject. Students can use a table of random numbers to make a set of index cards with 12 numbers on each card. They should use a different index card for each portion of the experiment. The cards can have a list of random letters or words instead of numbers. Music can be used in the background as a distraction during the test for auditory learning. The colored index cards, highlighters, and colored pencils can be used in the test for visual learning. The tray of objects can be used as a simple test to compare the three modes for each individual.

Preparation Tips

■ Collect various items that can be displayed on the trays in advance. Students will need enough variety so that they can have up to 12 different items on the tray for each part of the experiment.

Open It Up Encourage your students to think of ways to quickly test a person's learning: memorizing numbers or words, remembering items seen, listing the features of an object or person, etc.

Guiding Your Students

■ Once students determine a learning exercise, have them determine ways of presenting the exercise, emphasizing the three learning styles, and recording their results.

Interpret Your Data

1. Check to make sure that students correctly graph the data in their tables.

2. Student answers will vary but should reflect an understanding of learning styles and the student's own personal strengths.

Conclude and Apply

1. Student answers will vary. Some students might discover an area of strength in one mode; others might find that they use all three modes almost equally.

2. Student answers will vary, but could include: being hungry, tired, or anxious; not feeling well; learning curve; or use of strategies for remembering.

3. Student answers will vary, but might include modifying the way they review notes and study for tests.

Going Further

Student experiments will vary, but should demonstrate an understanding of inquiry and the results of the experiment just completed.

Activity 6

Purpose Students will learn about the importance of plant adaptations to their environments.

Skills Reinforced organizing, forming hypotheses, predicting, testing a hypothesis, observing, making and using tables, analyzing results, recognizing cause and effect, drawing conclusions, computer skills

Time Required 45 minutes to plan the activity; two weeks or more for the investigation; 45 minutes for analyzing the results

Background Plants first evolved in the ocean. Aquatic plants are supported by water and have little need for strengthening tissue in their stems. They can absorb nutrients directly, and they can reproduce by releasing sperm and egg cells into the water. The adaptation to life on land meant that plants had to develop structures suitable for a dry environment. At first the plants were small and nonvascular, like the mosses we see today. Gradually, plants developed a vascular system of internal tubes called xylem and phloem that allows water and nutrients to flow through the plant. Land plants also have stronger stems to support them in air, and most land plants reproduce by seeds. Their extensive root systems absorb water and nutrients from the soil and anchor them securely in the ground. The leaves of land plants have a waxy coating called a cuticle to prevent water loss, and they have stomata on the underside to allow the exchange of carbon dioxide and oxygen.

Possible Procedure Students will work in small groups to investigate whether a plant's adaptations will allow it to survive in a different environment. Each group will choose one plant to investigate. They will observe characteristics of the plant and determine how the plant is suited to its environment. Students will then create a different environment for the plant and observe how well its adaptations allow it to survive. Afterwards, they will dissect the plant to observe internal adaptations of the plant.

Preparation Tips

- Obtain a collection of desert, aquatic, and household plants, or have each group obtain their own. Inexpensive aquatic plants, such as *Elodea*, are available from pet supply stores.

- Play sand can be purchased at hardware stores.

- Students may choose to place their plants in a warm, lighted environment. Arrange a location where the plant and a lamp can be placed undisturbed.

Open It Up Before starting the activity, have the class discuss how plant adaptations allow them to live in different environments. Afterwards, ask, "What would happen if you put a cactus in a watery environment? Which characteristics of the cactus would be helpful, and which would be harmful?" Encourage students to develop and answer their own "What if ..." questions.

Guiding Your Students

- Some students may benefit from having a list of adaptations that plants of different environments have. They can use these lists as a guide when observing their plant.

- Give students everyday analogies to help them understand the plant adaptations. For example, you can relate a vascular system to drinking juice with a straw. You can describe a land plant's cuticle as a coat that keeps moisture in the leaves.

Interpret Your Data

1. Answers will depend on which plant students choose to study.
2. Students should describe characteristics of their plant that make it well suited to its natural environment.
3. Answers should include information about the plant's temperature, availability of water, type of soil, and sunlight.
4. Students should explain how often plants were watered, whether there were periods of light and dark, and other ways they cared for their plants.

5. Most plants will not survive as well in a different environment. Students should describe their observations.

6. Answers will vary.

Conclude and Apply

1. Students should recognize that some adaptations will be beneficial to a plant in its new environment, and other adaptations will be harmful.

2. Class observations should show that, although plants thrive best in their natural environment, some are able to survive in different environments as long as they are provided with basic needs.

Going Further

Each member of a group should be involved in creating the presentation. Provide time for each group to show their presentation to the entire class. You may wish to have students answer the second Conclude and Apply question after the presentations.

Activity 7

Purpose Students will investigate the possible effects of ozone depletion, resulting in increased UVB radiation reaching Earth's surface, on terrestrial plants.

Skills Reinforced forming hypotheses, testing hypotheses, controlling variables, recognizing cause and effect, measuring, describing, observing, collecting data, developing explanations, making graphs, communicating

Time Required one period to set up the experiment; five to ten minutes a day for care of plants and observations; one period for final measurements, including dried plant biomass, and analysis of data

Background Studies have shown that increased UVB exposure in phytoplankton can lead to inhibition of photosynthesis which results in less primary production. Some species of phytoplankton are more resistant to UVB exposure and are not as vulnerable to its damaging effects. It has also been shown that increased exposure to UVB radiation can negatively affect growth rate and leaf production in terrestrial plants. Some plants may have more natural resistance to the effects of UVB radiation.

Possible Procedure Students can use plastic containers with holes in the bottom as planters. They should use an equal amount of soil for each seed. Students can compare the growth of at least two species of plants (possibly alfalfa, beans, tomatoes, or peas) under different experimental conditions. An outdoor setup could compare plants grown under normal sun

conditions, plants grown under a UVB screen, and plants grown in the direct sunlight with an additional UVB source. Have students use extreme caution when using an electric light source outside. Limit the experiment to totally dry conditions, with the UVB light source being brought indoors at the end of every school day. Students can decide how much exposure the plants should receive each day. Use a drying oven to dry plants, then measure total biomass using the balance. Extended experiments could focus more specifically on any interaction between increased UVB radiation and herbivore activity or disease vulnerability, or the stage at which a plant is most vulnerable to overexposure to UVB radiation.

Preparation Tips

- Obtain seeds locally or order from a supply catalog in advance. If fungicide has been applied to seeds, students should wash their hands after handling them.
- Check the basic growth needs of the plants. You will need to determine the best watering and nutrient schedule.
- Obtain soil and nutrient supplements in advance.
- Obtain a UVB screen and UVB light in advance. Use only safe UVB bulbs. Some UVB bulbs can cause eye damage. Obtain appropriate fixtures for using the light outdoors.

Open It Up Encourage students to consider the many plant characteristics that could be affected by UVB radiation and to choose those that they could include in an experiment.

Guiding Your Students

- Help your students decide on the location for their study. The UVB light source must be extremely close to the plants (3–6 inches) to have any effect.
- Make sure students consider each species' water, light, and soil requirements when they plan their procedure.

Interpret Your Data

1. Check to make sure that students correctly graph the data in their tables.

2. Answers will vary. Students will probably see differences between control plants and experimental plants.

3. Depending on the type of plants used, students may find that plants under the UVB light showed decreased growth rates, smaller leaf size, a change in leaf morphology, or smaller biomass compared to the plants in other experimental conditions. In some cases, if a plant has some resistance to UVB light, the differences may not be significant.

Conclude and Apply

1. Increased exposure to UVB radiation could negatively impact any aspect of plant growth, primary production, or interaction between plants and other organisms leading to changes in an ecosystem.
2. Phytoplankton are the base of the food chain in water ecosystems. If production is reduced there could be less food for consumers at higher levels on the food chain.
3. Answers will vary but may include: selectively breeding crop plants that are more resistant to UVB radiation, using filters that remove UVB radiation to grow plants, and continue to educate the public about the ozone layer.
4. Continue to selectively breed plants from each generation that show the best growth under increased UVB radiation.

Going Further

Students may make a multimedia presentation including overhead projectors, spreadsheets, videos, or pamphlets that address the issue of ozone depletion.

Activity 8

Purpose Students will survey a small area of two ecosystems, calculate biodiversity, and compare the values for the two ecosystems.

Skills Reinforced forming hypotheses, testing hypotheses, collecting data, describing, observing, comparing and contrasting, communicating

Time Required one-half period to set up the activity; time outside of class to conduct the surveys; one period for final calculations and analyzing data

Background A large-scale pattern of species diversity emerges as species numbers are compared across lines of latitude. Tropical areas have much higher species diversity than do temperate and polar regions, with polar regions having the lowest species diversity. Although there are several possible explanations of why this pattern occurs, the most common is that tropical communities are older and have suffered fewer disturbances, such as glaciations, than temperate and polar communities. A tropical climate also has a longer growing season than temperate and polar climates.

Possible Procedure Students work alone or in groups of two. Students construct the quadrats using the string. Encourage students to develop a way to randomize the placement of their quadrats. For example, they might draw a simple map of the area they are sampling, divide

the map into numbered squares, and draw a number from a hat to determine where to place their quadrats. Encourage students to allow a few minutes to pass after they have arranged the quadrat to reduce the effects of disturbance before conducting their surveys.

Preparation Tips

- Review with students the importance of wearing gloves while conducting the surveys. They should not touch any plants or other living material without gloves.
- Appropriate field clothing includes wearing gloves, a wide-brim hat, long sleeves, long pants, thick socks, and sturdy, high-top walking/hiking shoes.
- Everyone should use waterproof sunscreen as directed.
- Make sure students drink sufficient amounts of water or non-caffeinated drinks.
- Review any other safety procedures that you would like students to follow.

Open It Up Encourage students to conduct each survey under the most similar conditions possible, such as the time of day and weather conditions. Also, encourage students to conduct more than one survey within each ecosystem to allow a more accurate representation of the type and number of organisms to be obtained. Allow interested students to pursue other biodiversity questions as they arise.

Guiding Your Students

Explain how to determine the Simpson Diversity Index.
- Add the numbers of each type of organism found in your survey to determine the total number of organisms.
- The proportion of each type of organism can be calculated by dividing the number of individual organisms found for each type by the total number of all types of organisms.
- Square each proportion.
- Add all of the squares of each proportion.
- Subtract this number from the number 1. This number is the Simpson Diversity Index value for the area surveyed.

Interpret Your Data

1. Check to make sure that students have calculated biodiversity correctly.
2. When students calculate the index value, they should get a number between 0 and 1. Students should conclude that a greater number indicates greater species diversity.

Copyright © by Glencoe/McGraw-Hill, a division of the McGraw-Hill Companies, Inc.

Conclude and Apply

1. Student answers will vary depending on which ecosystems they studied.

2. Students might be able to reach conclusions about certain ecosystems if enough data are compared.

3. Conducting multiple surveys allows for a more accurate representation of the species and their numbers.

4. Monitoring changes in biodiversity can be helpful in determining the health of an ecosystem.

Going Further

Students can share their presentation with other classes at their school or make their presentation to a middle school science class.

Activity 9

Purpose Students will understand the relationship between water quality and the health of different organisms in an ecosystem.

Skills Reinforced forming hypotheses, testing hypotheses, controlling variables, recognizing cause and effect, measuring, describing, collecting data, making graphs, developing explanations

Time Required one period to set up the activity; one-half to a whole period each day for five more days to make observations and monitor the number of organisms; one period for final counts and analyzing data

Background Certain types of protists can thrive in polluted water. Identifying the species and number of each type of organism in an area can be useful in determining water quality. Other species of protists are sensitive to changes in water quality such as the input of pesticides, heavy metals, and acid precipitation. Their absence from an environment in which they normally would thrive can indicate the presence of a pollutant.

Possible Procedure Students can work in groups of two. Students establish several cultures of each organism to be tested in glass jars. Each jar should receive the same treatment, except for the independent variable. Students can monitor the number of organisms by examining a 0.1–0.5-mL sample under the microscope each day for at least five days.

Preparation Tips

■ Obtain the necessary materials, such as liquid fertilizer, motor oil, and houseplant pesticide, in advance.

■ Order the organisms and, if applicable, the appropriate culture media from a supply catalog in

advance. Schedule delivery for the day before the experiment will begin.

■ Only GFCI protected electrical outlets should be used in areas where water is present.

Open It Up Encourage students to consider the wide range of options for this investigation and to narrow the number of organisms and pollutants to manageable numbers. Have the students consider the need to monitor the pH and temperature of the water for each set of organisms as the experiment continues. Also, have the students consider how to ensure that any substance added does not contain additional unrecorded chemicals or pollutants.

Guiding Your Students

■ Remind students that acid precipitation has a pH of less than 5.6.

■ Review with students any safety concerns for the lab and how you would like them to dispose of the materials used during the lab.

Interpret Your Data

1. Check to make certain that students correctly graph the data in their tables.

2. Student answers will vary depending on the type of organisms used and the outcome of the experiment.

Conclude and Apply

1. Student answers will vary but may include: differences in the amount of any substance introduced into the water, a different method of counting the organisms, unforeseen contamination, or human error. Conclusions will vary. Some organisms may show a decrease in number compared to the control group; some organisms that are more tolerant may not be affected.

2. Some organisms may be able to tolerate certain types of changes in water quality.

3. Any significant change in population can lead to a change in the dynamics of the ecosystem. Other organisms may not have enough food, species composition may change, and competition between organisms may increase.

4. Protists can be used as bioindicators. Different degrees of sensitivity for chemicals are determined for each organism. The organism that is the most sensitive to a given substance is used as a bioindicator.

Going Further

Experiments should determine which organism is the most sensitive to a given substance.

Activity 10

Purpose Students will investigate the best conditions for raising tadpoles.

Skills Reinforced researching information, making a Venn diagram, forming hypotheses, testing a hypothesis, identifying and manipulating variables and controls, observing, making tables, comparing and contrasting, recognizing cause and effect, drawing conclusions, evaluating others' data and conclusions, communicating, using graphics software

Time Required 45 minutes to plan the activity; a couple of minutes each day for 1 to 2 months for feeding and observations; 45 minutes for analyzing results

Background The best conditions for raising tadpoles depend on the species. Generally, the water should be about 18°C to 24°C. Old leaves can be placed in the bottom of the tadpoles' container. Each day, tadpoles should be fed several pinches of boiled lettuce or spinach leaves, flake goldfish food, or other food obtained from a pet store. The length of time required for metamorphosis probably will be about 2 months. However, it can be shorter or much longer depending on the environment and the species. Warmer water tends to increase the rate of metamorphosis.

Possible Procedure Students work in small groups to research appropriate conditions for raising tadpoles. Each group investigates one characteristic of the tadpole environment, such as temperature, water, food, light, or population density of tadpoles. Students may observe their tadpoles for all or part of the metamorphosis period. By varying one characteristic of the environment and comparing their results to a control group, students learn about good conditions for raising tadpoles.

Preparation Tips

■ Tap water can be used if you add a water conditioner obtained from a pet shop. Alternatively, you can let the tap water sit for at least 4 days before using it. Be sure to keep a good supply of prepared water on hand. About once a month, one-fourth of the water used in the tadpole tank should be drained and replaced.

■ Decide on a suitable source for tadpoles. Fast-growing tadpoles can be obtained from biological supply companies. You may also wish to have students obtain tadpoles from a nearby pond.

■ Check with local wildlife officials about regulations for collecting tadpoles and releasing frogs into the environment.

■ Only GFCI protected electrical outlets should be used in areas where water is present.

Open It Up After students have researched the proper care conditions for tadpoles, have them make a list on the chalkboard of the characteristics of a tadpole's environment, such as water and food. Beside each characteristic, have them write ways that the characteristic could be changed. Allow interested students to pursue other questions that arise.

Guiding Your Students

■ Explain to students that they won't be able to conduct a comprehensive study of the best conditions for raising tadpoles. Instead, they should focus on a narrow question, such as, "Do tadpoles thrive better at 18°C or 24°C?"

■ Other topics that students might study: Which type of food works best? Does the number of tadpoles in the tank adversely affect tadpole growth? Is pond water or spring water better for their growth? Do some types of tadpoles thrive better in captivity than other types?

Interpret Your Data

1. Students probably will observe the tadpoles gradually metamorphosing into frogs.
2. Students should understand that both the control group and the experimental group probably will mature. Their response should note differences in the rate of maturation and differences in the well-being of the tadpoles.
3. Check students' responses.
4. Check to be sure the diagrams accurately reflect conditions recorded in students' observation table.

Conclude and Apply

1. Students should mention similarities and differences in the rate of maturation and the well-being of the tadpoles.
2. Students should explain which condition they tested and which group responded best.
3. Answers might describe no differences, slight differences, or significant differences between the condition of the control group and the experimental group.
4. Students may wish they could test other variations of the characteristic they tested, such as different temperatures or foods, or other water conditions.
5. Overall, the class should conclude that tadpoles thrive best in water that is allowed to be a bit cloudy. The food should be small bits of plants, such as lettuce leaves, when the tadpole is young. As a tadpole nears the change to a frog, its diet should be more carnivorous.

Going Further

Students should not include details about their individual investigation in the instructional booklets. They should only include the results obtained by the entire class.